DOGS
A GLOBAL ALPHABET

Ralph Wright, OSB

Illustrations by Barbara Martin Smith

MONOGRAPH PUBLISHING

Design by Ellie Jones and William E. Mathis
        MathisJones Communications, LLC

Library of Congress Cataloging-in-Publication Data
ISBN 978-0-9964948-5-4

Published by Monograph Publishing, LLC
1 Putt Lane
Eureka, Missouri 63025
info@mathisjones.com
monographpublishing.com

Printed and bound in the United States of America

About the Author

Fr. Ralph Wright was born in Nottinghamshire, England on October 13, 1938, and joined the Benedictine abbey of Ampleforth in September of 1959. Having completed his BA in Greats (Classics, Ancient History and Philosophy) at Oxford and his STL (Sacrae Theologiae Licentiatus) degree in Theology at Fribourg (Switzerland), he was ordained a priest on July 5, 1970. A month later, at the abbot's invitation, he left England to join the St. Louis Priory, the community's foundation in the United States. Initially, Fr. Ralph taught Latin, Greek, English and Religion in the St. Louis Priory School. He currently teaches Creative Writing to seniors, is Vocation Director for the monastery and an assistant to the Varsity tennis coach.

About the Artist

Barbara was born and raised in the heartland of the United States to a family who celebrated the value of a quality education in the arts. She has spent her life playing with paint and sharing respect for creative expression in the arts.

As a young woman, she adored her family pets, later delighting in her children's devotion to the family's and extended family's cats, dogs, lamas, and horses. Portraits of her Sovereign Standard Poodle have inspired others to commission portraits of their beloved animals. The American Kennel Club Museum of the Dog lists her on their "ARTISTS REGISTRY." Her poodle has been invited to be the visiting dog of the day and she has been invited to be a visiting artist.

Her watercolors continue a theme, SCAPES, which she developed during her work for her Master of Fine Arts Degree. Her SOULSCAPES paintings capture the spirit of the subject's soul through gesture and expression, and the DOG portraits in this book capture the character of each dog in Father Ralph's poems. All are rhythmscapes, merging the fluidity of the watercolor medium on handmade paper with the transience of treasured moments.

Barbara's career began as an art educator teaching briefly in the Dominica in the Caribbean Islands. She has worked in public, private, and museum education, most recently as a teacher at The Villa Duchesne Oak Hill School and as a volunteer docent at The Saint Louis Art Museum.

An award winning artist and art educator, she has exhibited her watercolor paintings and won top awards both nationally and locally in competitive and solo exhibitions, and her art work is included in corporate and private collections. She has been honored to be named International Woman of the Year in Recognition of her services to Art Education by The International Biographical Centre of Cambridge, England. She has been chosen numerous times for inclusion in Marquis Who's Who in American Education. Additionally, she accepted the awesome invitation to be a guest of the Japanese Ministry of Culture as a member of the First Art Education Delegation to Japan with the People to People Eisenhower Professional Exchange.

CONTENTS

DEDICATION

To the memory

of

Gertrude "Trudy" Barry

July 20, 1929 – April 17, 2015

a gentle woman

who loved

her God, her family and her dogs

I'm an Afghan hound.
I'm a bit of a snob.
I may look aloof
but I think like God.

B

I'm Winston
of Bulldog fame.
My only glamor
is my famous name.

I'm a Cocker Spaniel,
call me Copper.
When we're at Burger King
I get me a whopper.

I'm Dusty the Husky,
an Alaskan breed.
We move as a team
with Lexus speed.

I'm Evan the Collie,
I always obey.
I fetch his sheep
three fields away.

I'm Sigmund
a Dachshund.
When they're annoyed
they call me Freud.

I'm a German Shepherd,
Maggie by name.
I guard our nation
without shame.

German
Shepherd
Barbara Morton Smith

I'm Barry,
a Basset Hound.
I tread on my ears
as I move around.

I'm a Kerry Beagle
with an Irish tang.
I worship Snoopy
who was never wrong.

I'm James,
a Great Dane.
I'm a gracious Goliath,
gentle as rain.

I'm a King Charles Spaniel,
— well bred.
(It's not the Charles
who lost his head.)

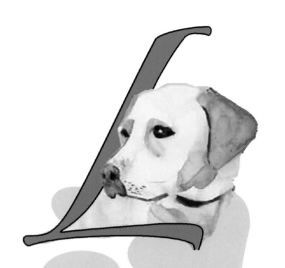

I'm a yellow Lab
with a meltdown boss—
"Joss, come here!
Come here, Joss!
Joss, WILL you come here!
Joss!"

M

I'm a Mutt,
spelt ~u.t.t.
I don't know my parents
and they don't know me.

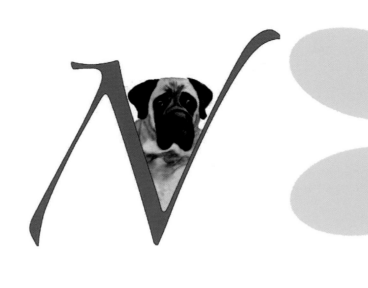

I'm a Bullmastiff,
Nasty by name.
If you bother me,
I'm not to blame.

Otto the Pekingese
is sorry to say
he can't write Otto
the Chinese way.

I'm Shadow,
a dark Poodle.
If you want my stats
you'll have to google.

I'm a full grown Chihuahua
from Quebec.
If you're looking for more
this is all you'll get.

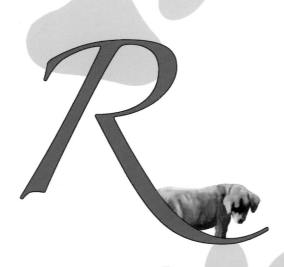

R

I'm Hector,
a Golden Retriever.
In Ultimate Frisbee
I'm a great receiver.

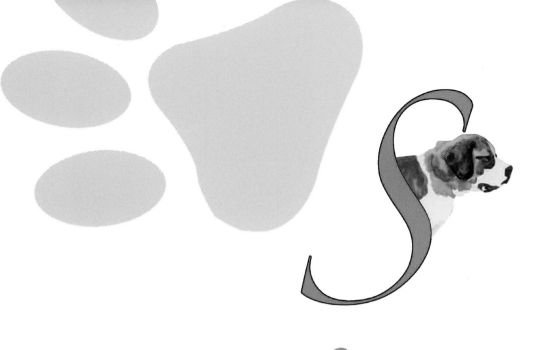

I'm a Saint Bernard,
brandy 'n all.
I warm a climber
when he's had a fall.

I'm a Shih Tzu,
a tiny hound.
I get lost easily
but bark till I'm found.

I'm a Rottweiler,
Uri the Mean.
My bark brings terror
To the burglar's spleen.

I'm a Doberman Pinscher,
Vince by name.
I've Medusa eyes
and my fangs are insane.

I'm Tripp the Whippet.
I move real fast.
That blur was me
flying past.

We're Xceptional terriers,
Scottie and White.
The Queen Mother
used to hold us tight.

I'm a Yorkshire terrier,
one ball of hair.
If I'm going backwards,
beware! Beware!

I'm a Bloodhound tracker
from Zanzibar.

I track DNA,
50 bucks an hour.

FOOTNOTES AND MEMORIES
by Fr. Ralph

Anne Porter
The German Shepherd painting is of Maggie, Anne Porter's dog. Anne lived
on Long Island with her husband, Fairfield Porter, a well-known artist in New York
who died in 1975. Anne's poetry was first published in 1994. Through a review of her book I came to
know her and greatly admired her poetry. I used to visit her every other year till around 2011. She died
at the age of 99 and eleven months. She was a remarkable woman of great gentleness and wisdom,
and an excellent poet whose work deserves wider recognition.

Guy Jackson
The poem about Joss was written back in 1966 at the death of
Guy Jackson. He was a great friend of our family who won an M.C. in the 1914-18 war.
He used to organize grouse shoots on Beeley moor. For nine years,
he was captain of the Derbyshire cricket team. Joss was his yellow lab.

Trudy Barry
This poem was written when Trudy's poodle, Shadow, died.

The following poems are in memory of these dear friends...

THE GOSPEL ACCORDING TO ANNE

the way you looked at me
with a wicked gentleness
before giving the oracle

the way you scraped and chopped
the carrots

the weathered patience in your voice
as you declared that Maggie
—your arthritic elderly German Shepherd—
deserved a medal
for lumbering painfully up the stairs to your room
last night
for a drink of water

and told how last year
you gave up
paranoia for Lent

and the way you said
'Sinners are God's special people'

did not leave much more
in any language
that needed to be spoken

57

GUY – A MEMORY

Beeley the morning mist and grouse
complaining against aggression

welsh laughter partridges and trout
and Cherry Brandy

moments of cricket sunshine clapping warmth
and a carefree
calm and relaxed enjoyment life being there
given surely above all by God
to be lived, loved and laughed by

how clear is the memory of a man
we loved, lived and laughed with
is there a single call that now
can
somehow
echo our loss?
'Joss, come here!
Come here, Joss!
Joss, WILL you come here!
Joss!'

58

SHADOW

O where O
where
has Shadow gone
O where O where
can she be
she has left
the world
for the sun
has gone
and taken my Shadow from me.

Other Fine Works
by Fr. Ralph

Ripples of Stillness
Life is Simpler Toward Evening
Perhaps God
Seamless
All the Stars are Snowflakes
Verticle Thoughts
Of Leaves, Flowers and Trees
Leaves of Water
Christ—Our Love for All Seasons
Our Daily Bread
Wild...
Wilder...
Wildest...
Eloquence of Truth
They Also Serve: Tennis, a Global Religion
Over 50 Hymns